... the

BALANCE BOOK

... by

Lee Jenkins

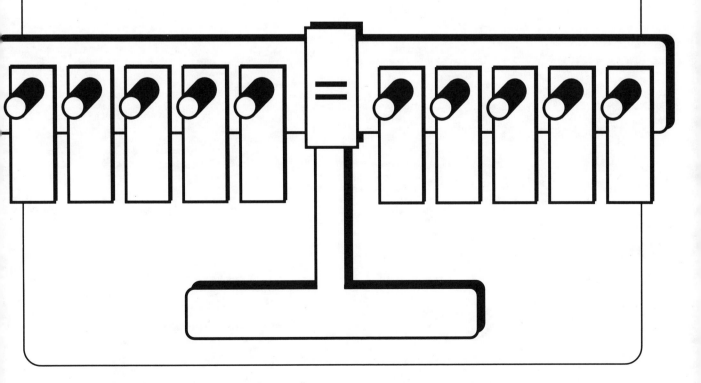

No part of this book may be duplicated ...

except for assorted weights and student designed activity pages. These may be duplicated by a teacher for classroom use.

... the Balance Book
ISBN 0-941530-45-0
(previously ISBN 0-918932-02-5)

DIRECTIONS AND ANSWERS

These activity cards are designed to be placed in a 5'' x 8'' file box. The title section of the front cover can be glued on the outside of a file box.

Two index cards with tabs are provided on the back cover and the other index tab cards are provided inside this book. For all the activity cards the numeral inside the weight indicates where the student is to place the weight(s).

ADDITION, 1-8: Students may need to be shown that the addition problem is represented with weights on the left side of the balance and the answer with a weight on the right side of the balance. On activity 4 students may need help representing 11 as one weight on 10 and one weight on 1.

MULTIPLICATION, 9-18: Multiplication on the math balance is repeated addition. 3 x 4 on the math balance in interpreted as, "Three weights on 4 is balanced by what"? Students will need to be shown to place as many weights on the ten as possible. Thirty-two can be represented many ways on the math balance, but when a student is solving 4 x 8, two plus three 10's is the easiest answer to read. Students can solve activities 17 and 18 without asking about the title — Square Numbers. Should they inquire, square numbers can be explained by having students cut different size squares out of graph paper. They will find that these large squares have 1, 4, 9, 16, 25 . . . little squares in them. Answers: 1+3=2x2;   1+3+5=3x3;   1+3+5+7=4x4; 1+3+5+7+9=5x5; 1+3+5+7+9+11=6x6.

OTHER NAMES, 19-22: Students are to represent the numbers 12, 16, 18 and 9 on one side of the balance and record ten ways they balanced each number using as many weights as desired.

TENS, 23-30: These activities are designed to reinforce the concept of 10 in our decimal number system. The second problem on activity 26 is impossible. Students should be encouraged to solve this problem until they are positive that it is impossible.

DIVISION, 31-42: 12 ÷ 3 on the math balance is interpreted, "How many 3's does it take to balance 12?" The division problems are written in three forms— $3\overline{)12}$ is read, "Twelve divided by three," 12 ÷ 3 is read, "Twelve divided by three," and $\frac{12}{3}$ is also read, "Twelve divided by three." Many of the problems on activities 41 and 42 have remainders. A child solving 19 ÷ 5 discovers that three 5's won't balance 19 and four 5's is too heavy. However, three 5's and one 4 will balance 19. This can be expressed as 3 r4.

ADDITION PROBLEM SOLVING, 51-58: Students are to place one weight on each weight diagram. On Activity 51 the student is to attempt to balance the numbers 1-10 with four weights—three of which can be put on 1 and one which can be put on 6. Not all of the numerals can be balanced with the weights specified and the students are instructed to circle those that can be balanced.

Answers:

```
51   ①②③ 4  5  ⑥⑦⑧⑨ 10
52   1 ② 3 ④ 5 ⑥ 7 ⑧ 9 10
53   ①②③ 4 ⑤⑥⑦⑧ 9 10
54   1 ②③ 4 ⑤ 6 ⑦⑧ 9 ⑩ 11 ⑫⑬ 14 ⑮ 16 ⑰⑱ 19 ⑳
55   1 ②③ 4 ⑤ 6 ⑦⑧ 9 ⑩ 11 ⑫⑬ 14 ⑮ 16 ⑰⑱ 19 ⑳
56   ①②③④⑤⑥⑦⑧⑨⑩⑪⑫⑬⑭⑮ 16 17 18 19 20
57   ① 2 3 4 ⑤⑥ 7 ⑧⑨⑩⑪ 12 ⑬⑭⑮⑯ 17 ⑱⑲ 20 21 22 ㉓㉔ 25 26 27 28 29 30
58   1 2 3 4 ⑤ 6 7 8 ⑨⑩ 11 12 13 ⑭⑮ 16 17 18 ⑲⑳ 21 22 23 ㉔㉕ 26 27 28 ㉙ 30
     31 32 33 ㉞ 35 36 37 38 39 40
```

MULTIPLICATION LOGIC, 59-66: Students who place the weights on the balance in a logical, systematic manner will be able to solve these problems rather quickly.

Answers:
59. 1. 2x3=3x2 2. 2x6=3x4 3. 2x9=3x6   63. 1. (4x2)+2=5x2 2. (4x7)+2=5x6
60. 1. 2x6=4x3 2. 2x8=4x4   64. many possible answers
61. 1. 3x4=4x3 2. 3x8=4x6   65. 1. 3x1=(2x1)+1 2. 3x3=(2x4)+1 3. 3x5=(2x7)+1 4. 3x7=(2x10)+1
62. 1. 4x5=5x4 2. 4x10=5x8   66. 1. (4x1)+2=6x1 2. (4x4)+2=6x3 3. (4x7)+2=6x5 4. (4x10)+2=6x7

BALANCE, 67-76: Students can be asked to record all of their estimates before going to the math balance to check their estimates. Answers: 67—no, yes; 68—no, yes; 69—10, 1; 70—7, impossible; 71—4, 3; 72—3, 3; 73—4, 9; 74—12, 3; 75—4, 5; 76—9, 8.

PLACE VALUE, 43-46: On all four place value activities the students are to balance the numbers at the right of the page using only the weights designated. For activity 43, the student is to balance the numbers 1-15 with only four weights — one which can be only put on 1, one which can only be put on 2, one which can only be put on 4 and one which can only be put on 8. Thus 1 is balanced with a weight on 1, 2 is balanced with a weight on two and no weights on 1, three is balanced with a weight on 2 and 1. For activity 44, the numbers 1-16 are to be balanced using eight weights — four which can be used on 1 and four which can be used on 5. Activity 45 asks the students to balance the odd numbers between 1 and 27 with six weights — two on 1, two on 3, and two on 9. For activity 46 the students are to balance the multiples of five from 5 to 70 with fourteen weights — seven on 1 and seven on 8.

		43				44				45				46	
8	4	2	1		5	1		9	3	1		8	1	
			1	1		1	1			1	1		5	5
		1	0	2		2	3		1	0	3	1	2	10
		1	1	3		3	5		1	2	5	1	7	15
	1	0	0	4		4	7		2	1	7	2	4	20
	1	0	1	5	1	0	9	1	0	0	9	3	1	25
	1	1	0	6	1	1	11	1	0	2	11	3	6	30
	1	1	1	7	1	2	13	1	1	1	13	4	3	35
1	0	0	0	8	1	3	15	1	2	0	15	5	0	40
1	0	0	1	9	1	4	17	1	2	2	17	5	5	45
1	0	1	0	10	2	0	19	2	0	1	19	6	2	50
1	0	1	1	11	2	1	21	2	1	0	21	6	7	55
1	1	0	0	12	2	2	23	2	1	2	23	7	4	60
1	1	0	1	13	2	3	25	2	2	1	25	impossible		65
1	1	1	0	14	2	4	27	impossible			27	impossible		70
1	1	1	1	15	3	0								

COLORING PATTERNS, 47-50: After the students begin to color in the squares they may see the pattern and continue to color without the aid of the math balance.

AND/OR LOGIC, 77-86: Each of these activities have three questions. For example, activity 79 asks the student to balance 16 with weights on 3 and 4. The student must place weights on both the 3 and the 4. Next the student must place weights either on the three or the four. Finally the student must balance 16 without the use of three or four. Some correct answers are:

77. 2+3+3=8; 4x2=8; 4+4=8
78. 2+2+2+3+3=12; 4x3=12; 7+5=12
79. 3+3+3+3+4=16; 4x4=16; 9+5+2=16
80. (5x3)+5=20; 5x4=20; 10x2=20
81. 9+9+6=24; 6x4=24; 3x8=24

82. (5x2)+(3x5)=25; 5x5=25; 7+8+10=25
83. 3+3+3+3+4+5=21; 7x3=21; 6+7+8=21
84. 3+4+5+5+5+5=27; 9x3=27; 10+10+7=27
85. 6+5+5+4+4+4=28; 9x4=28; 9+9+2+8=28
86. 4+4+5+5+6+6=30; 5x6=30; 9+9+9+3=30

FACTORS, 87-94: The factors of 12, 13, 14, 15, 16 and 18 are recorded individually before this information is listed on activity cards 93 and 94. For activities 87-92 the students are to check "yes" or "no" if the numeral at the top of the page can be balanced with only weights on 1, then with weights only on 2, etc. Activity 93 asks the students to color all the yes answers on the chart. For activity 94 the students are to list the common factors. For example, the common factor for 12 and 11 is 1, for 12 and 13 is 1. The common factors for 12 and 14 are 1 and 2. Answers:

12 and 13	1	15 and 12	1, 3	16 and 12	1, 2, 4	14 and 12	1, 2
12 and 14	1, 2	15 and 13	1	16 and 13	1	14 and 13	1
12 and 15	1, 3	15 and 14	1	16 and 14	1, 2	14 and 15	1
12 and 16	1, 2, 4	15 and 16	1	16 and 15	1	14 and 16	1, 2
12 and 18	1, 2, 3, 6	15 and 18	1, 3	16 and 18	1, 2	14 and 18	1, 2

STUDENT DESIGNED ACTIVITY CARDS: The last three pages of this book are for student use in designing activity cards for fellow students or cross-age tutoring.

On the back of activities 93 and 94 are drawings of weights. Copies of this page should be duplicated to allow students to cut and paste in designing activity cards. The last page of this book can also be duplicated. It is blank activity cards. A friend of the student designer is to write his/her name in the space provided. This indicates that the friend has done the activity on the math balance and it is appropriate for the math balance.

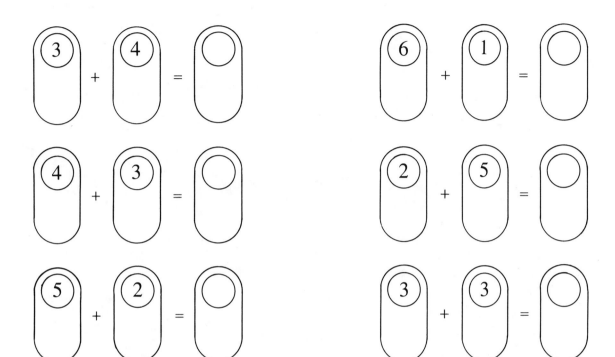

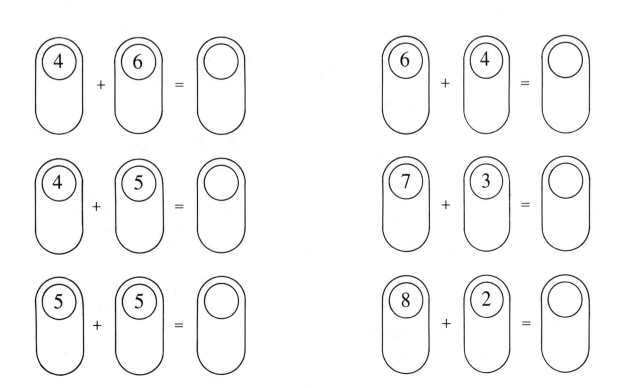

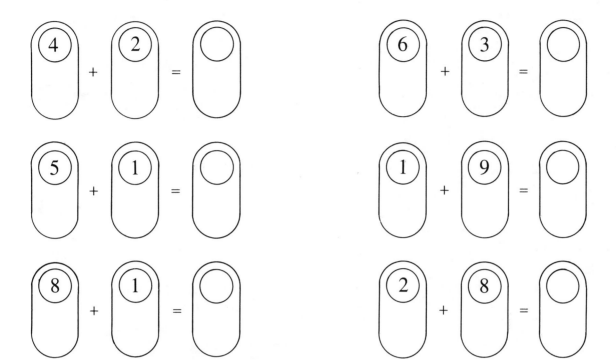

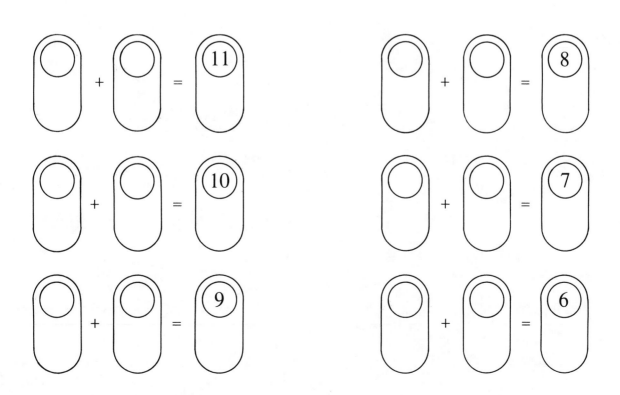

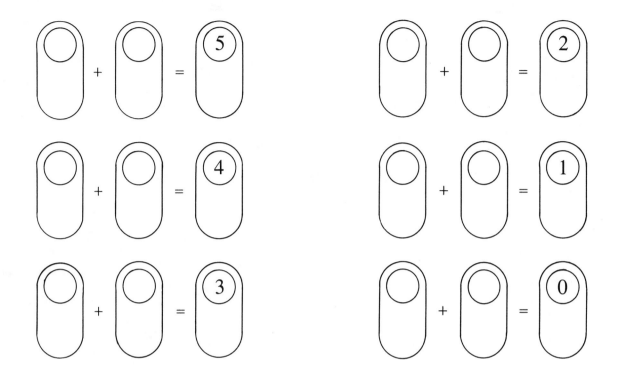

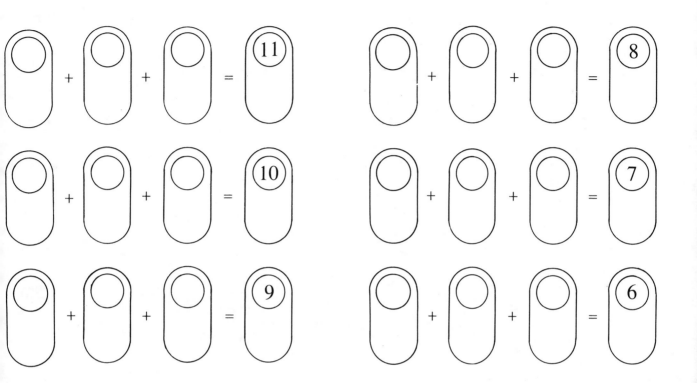

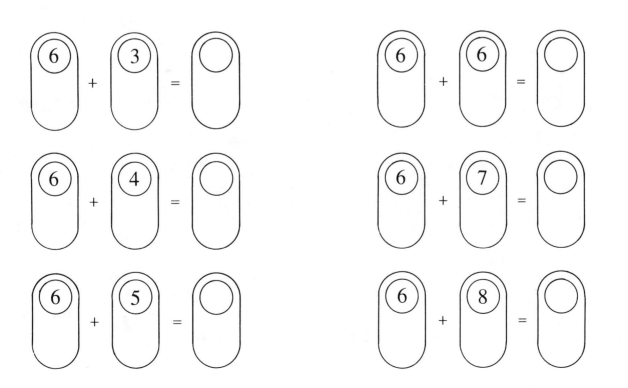

TASK 9
Multiplication

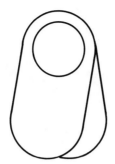

1. 2 x 1 = _____

2. 2 x 2 = _____

3. 2 x 3 = _____

4. 2 x 4 = _____

5. 2 x 5 = _____

6. 2 x 6 = _____

7. 2 x 7 = _____

8. 2 x 8 = _____

9. 2 x 9 = _____

10. 2 x 10 = _____

TASK 11
Multiplication

1. 4 x 1 = _____

2. 4 x 2 = _____

3. 4 x 3 = _____

4. 4 x 4 = _____

5. 4 x 5 = _____

6. 4 x 6 = _____

7. 4 x 7 = _____

8. 4 x 8 = _____

9. 4 x 9 = _____

10. 4 x 10 = _____

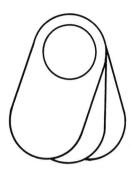

TASK 10
Multiplication

1. 3 x 1 = _____

2. 3 x 2 = _____

3. 3 x 3 = _____

4. 3 x 4 = _____

5. 3 x 5 = _____

6. 3 x 6 = _____

7. 3 x 7 = _____

8. 3 x 8 = _____

9. 3 x 9 = _____

10. 3 x 10 = _____

- -

TASK 12
Multiplication

1. 5 x 1 = _____

2. 5 x 2 = _____

3. 5 x 3 = _____

4. 5 x 4 = _____

5. 5 x 5 = _____

6. 5 x 6 = _____

7. 5 x 7 = _____

8. 5 x 8 = _____

9. 5 x 9 = _____

10. 5 x 10 = _____

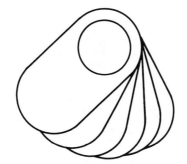

1. 6 x 1 = _____

2. 6 x 2 = _____

3. 6 x 3 = _____

4. 6 x 4 = _____

5. 6 x 5 = _____

6. 6 x 6 = _____

7. 6 x 7 = _____

8. 6 x 8 = _____

9. 6 x 9 = _____

10. 6 x 10 = _____

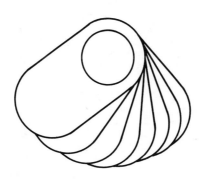

1. 8 x 1 = _____

2. 8 x 2 = _____

3. 8 x 3 = _____

4. 8 x 4 = _____

5. 8 x 5 = _____

6. 8 x 6 = _____

7. 8 x 7 = _____

8. 8 x 8 = _____

9. 8 x 9 = _____

10. 8 x 10 = _____

TASK 14
Multiplication

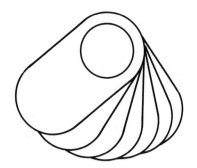

1. 7 x 1 = _____

2. 7 x 2 = _____

3. 7 x 3 = _____

4. 7 x 4 = _____

5. 7 x 5 = _____

6. 7 x 6 = _____

7. 7 x 7 = _____

8. 7 x 8 = _____

9. 7 x 9 = _____

10. 7 x 10 = _____

TASK 16
Multiplication

1. 9 x 1 = _____

2. 9 x 2 = _____

3. 9 x 3 = _____

4. 9 x 4 = _____

5. 9 x 5 = _____

6. 9 x 6 = _____

7. 9 x 7 = _____

8. 9 x 8 = _____

9. 9 x 9 = _____

10. 9 x 10 = _____

TASK 17
Square Numbers

$$\boxed{1} + \boxed{3} = \bigcirc$$

$$\boxed{1} + \boxed{3} + \boxed{5} = \bigcirc$$

$$\boxed{1} + \boxed{3} + \boxed{5} + \boxed{7} = \bigcirc$$

- -

TASK 19
Other Names

$$\boxed{10} \qquad \boxed{2}$$

Balance 12

1. _____ = 12   6. _____ = 12

2. _____ = 12   7. _____ = 12

3. _____ = 12   8. _____ = 12

4. _____ = 12   9. _____ = 12

5. _____ = 12   10. _____ = 12

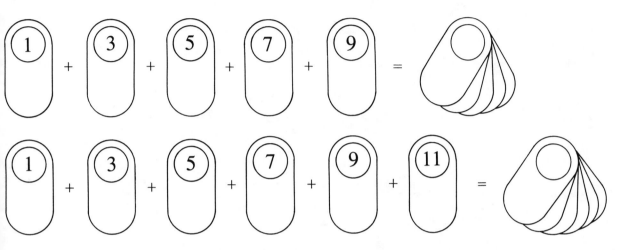

Balance 16

1. _____ = 16   6. _____ = 16

2. _____ = 16   7. _____ = 16

3. _____ = 16   8. _____ = 16

4. _____ = 16   9. _____ = 16

5. _____ = 16   10. _____ = 16

Balance 18

1. _____ = 18   6. _____ = 18

2. _____ = 18   7. _____ = 18

3. _____ = 18   8. _____ = 18

4. _____ = 18   9. _____ = 18

5. _____ = 18   10. _____ = 18

- -

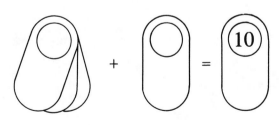

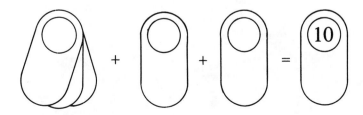

Balance 9

1. _____ = 9   6. _____ = 9

2. _____ = 9   7. _____ = 9

3. _____ = 9   8. _____ = 9

4. _____ = 9   9. _____ = 9

5. _____ = 9   10. _____ = 9

TASK 24
Tens

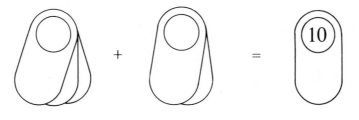

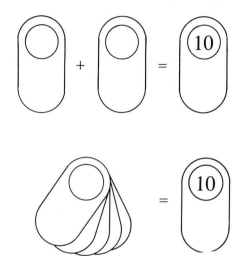

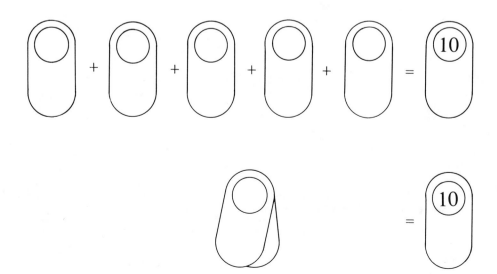

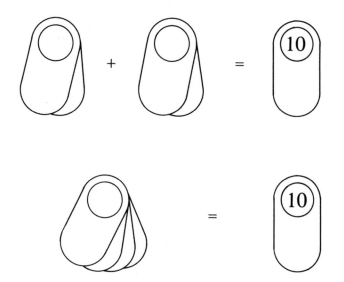

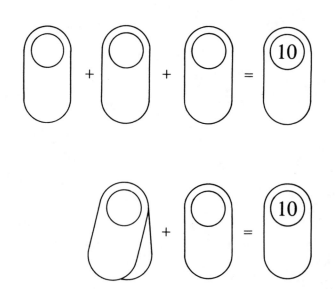

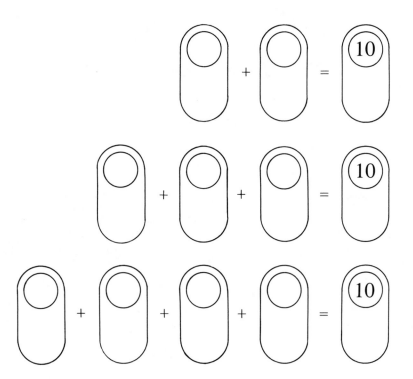

How many 2's does it take to balance 2?

1. $2 \div 2 =$ _____

2. $4 \div 2 =$ _____

3. $6 \div 2 =$ _____

4. $8 \div 2 =$ _____

5. $10 \div 2 =$ _____

6. $12 \div 2 =$ _____

7. $14 \div 2 =$ _____

8. $16 \div 2 =$ _____

9. $18 \div 2 =$ _____

10. $20 \div 2 =$ _____

◯ + ◯ + ◯ + ◯ + ◯ = ⑩

◯ + ◯ + ◯ + ◯ + ◯ + ◯ = ⑩

◯ + ◯ + ◯ + ◯ + ◯ + ◯ + ◯ + ◯ + ◯ = ⑩

- -

How many 3's does it take to balance 9?

1. $3\overline{)9}$ _____

2. $3\overline{)6}$ _____

3. $3\overline{)3}$ _____

4. $3\overline{)12}$ _____

5. $3\overline{)15}$ _____

6. $3\overline{)18}$ _____

7. $3\overline{)21}$ _____

8. $3\overline{)24}$ _____

9. $3\overline{)27}$ _____

10. $3\overline{)30}$ _____

1. $16 \div 4 =$ _____

2. $32 \div 4 =$ _____

3. $40 \div 4 =$ _____

4. $16 \div 4 =$ _____

5. $28 \div 4 =$ _____

6. $4\overline{)36}$ _____

7. $4\overline{)4}$ _____

8. $4\overline{)12}$ _____

9. $4\overline{)20}$ _____

10. $4\overline{)8}$ _____

1. $36 \div 6 =$ _____

2. $6\overline{)42} =$ _____

3. $\frac{54}{6} =$ _____

4. $\frac{6}{6} =$ _____

5. $6\overline{)18} =$ _____

6. $\frac{60}{6} =$ _____

7. $30 \div 6 =$ _____

8. $6\overline{)24} =$ _____

9. $48 \div 6 =$ _____

10. $6\overline{)12} =$ _____

1. $\frac{25}{5}$ = _____

2. $\frac{30}{5}$ = _____

3. $\frac{50}{5}$ = _____

4. $\frac{5}{5}$ = _____

5. $\frac{10}{5}$ = _____

6. $\frac{35}{5}$ = _____

7. $\frac{40}{5}$ = _____

8. $\frac{45}{5}$ = _____

9. $\frac{15}{5}$ = _____

10. $\frac{20}{5}$ = _____

TASK 36
Division

1. $7\overline{)7}$ _____

2. $7\overline{)14}$ _____

3. $7\overline{)21}$ _____

4. $7\overline{)28}$ _____

5. $7\overline{)35}$ _____

6. $7\overline{)42}$ _____

7. $7\overline{)50}$ _____

8. $7\overline{)56}$ _____

9. $7\overline{)63}$ _____

10. $7\overline{)70}$ _____

1. $8\overline{)64} =$ _____

2. $8\overline{)65} =$ _____

3. $\frac{64}{8} =$ _____

4. $\frac{16}{8} =$ _____

5. $\frac{24}{8} =$ _____

6. $\frac{24}{8} =$ _____

7. $32 \div 8 =$ _____

8. $32 \div 8 =$ _____

9. $72 \div 8 =$ _____

10. $72 \div 9 =$ _____

12

1. $12 \div 2 =$ _____

2. $12 \div 3 =$ _____

3. $12 \div 4 =$ _____

4. $12 \div 6 =$ _____

5. $12 \div 12 =$ _____

6. $12 \div 1 =$ _____

1. $9\overline{)81}$ = _____
2. $9\overline{)72}$ = _____
3. $8\overline{)72}$ = _____
4. $6\overline{)72}$ = _____
5. $7\overline{)70}$ = _____
6. $9\overline{)36}$ = _____
7. $9\overline{)27}$ = _____

8. $9\overline{)18}$ = _____
9. $6\overline{)18}$ = _____
10. $9\overline{)45}$ = _____
11. $9\overline{)54}$ = _____
12. $6\overline{)54}$ = _____
13. $9\overline{)27}$ = _____
14. $9\overline{)63}$ = _____

. 24

1. $24 \div 3$ = _____
2. $24 \div 4$ = _____
3. $24 \div 6$ = _____

4. $24 \div 8$ = _____
5. $24 \div 12$ = _____
6. $24 \div 2$ = _____

1. $5\overline{)8}$ = _____

2. $5\overline{)9}$ = _____

3. $5\overline{)10}$ = _____

4. $5\overline{)11}$ = _____

5. $5\overline{)12}$ = _____

6. $5\overline{)13}$ = _____

7. $5\overline{)14}$ = _____

8. $5\overline{)15}$ = _____

9. $5\overline{)16}$ = _____

10. $5\overline{)17}$ = _____

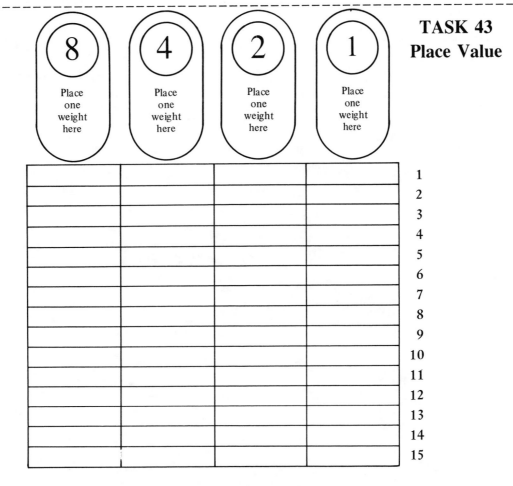

TASK 42
Division

1. $5\overline{)18}$ = _____

2. $5\overline{)19}$ = _____

3. $5\overline{)20}$ = _____

4. $5\overline{)21}$ = _____

5. $5\overline{)22}$ = _____

6. $5\overline{)23}$ = _____

7. $5\overline{)24}$ = _____

8. $5\overline{)25}$ = _____

9. $5\overline{)26}$ = _____

10. $5\overline{)27}$ = _____

TASK 44
Place Value

5 Place weight here	1 Place weight here	
		1
		2
		3
		4
		5
		6
		7
		8
		9
		10
		11
		12
		13
		14
		15

9	3	1
Place	Place	Place
weight here	weight here	weight here

			1
			3
			5
			7
			9
			11
			13
			15
			17
			19
			21
			23
			25
			27

Color the numbers below that can be balanced with weights on 2:

1	2	3	4	5
6	7	8	9	10
11	12	13	14	15
16	17	18	19	20
21	22	23	24	25
26	27	28	29	30

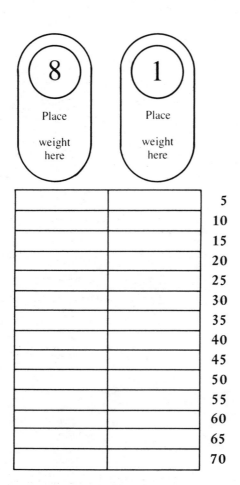

	5
	10
	15
	20
	25
	30
	35
	40
	45
	50
	55
	60
	65
	70

Color the numbers below that can be balanced with weights on 3:

1	2	3	4	5
6	7	8	9	10
11	12	13	14	15
16	17	18	19	20
21	22	23	24	25
26	27	28	29	30

Color the numbers below that can be balanced with weights on 4:

1	2	3	4	5	6	7
8	9	10	11	12	13	14
15	16	17	18	19	20	21
22	23	24	25	26	27	28
29	30	31	32	33	34	35
36	37	38	39	40	41	42
43	44	45	46	47	48	49

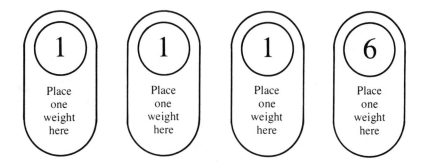

Circle the numbers below that can be balanced with the above weights.

1   2   3   4   5   6   7   8   9   10

Color the numbers below that can be balanced with weights on 5:

1	2	3	4	5	6	7
8	9	10	11	12	13	14
15	16	17	18	19	20	21
22	23	24	25	26	27	28
29	30	31	32	33	34	35
36	37	38	39	40	41	42
43	44	45	46	47	48	49

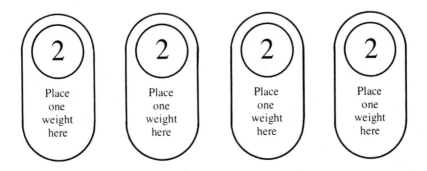

Circle the numbers below that can be balanced with the above weights.

1   2   3   4   5   6   7   8   9   10

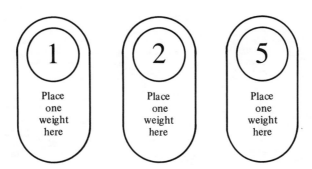

Circle the numbers below that can be balanced with the above weights.

1   2   3   4   5   6   7   8   9   10

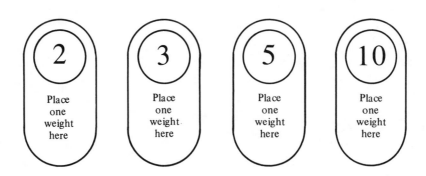

Circle the numbers below that can be balanced with the above weights.

1   2   3   4   5   6   7   8   9   10

11   12   13   14   15   16   17   18   19   20

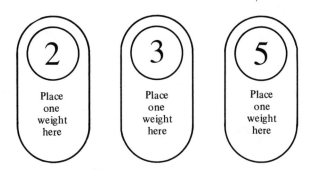

Circle the numbers below that can be balanced with the above weights.

1   2   3   4   5   6   7   8   9   10

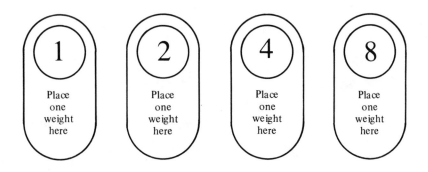

Circle the numbers below that can be balanced with the above weights.

1   2   3   4   5   6   7   8   9   10

11   12   13   14   15   16   17   18   19   20

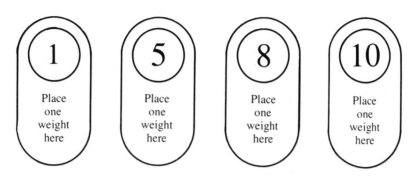

Circle the numbers below that can be balanced with the above weights.

1	2	3	4	5	6	7	8	9	10
11	12	13	14	15	16	17	18	19	20
21	22	23	24	25	26	27	28	29	30

TASK 59
Multiplication Logic

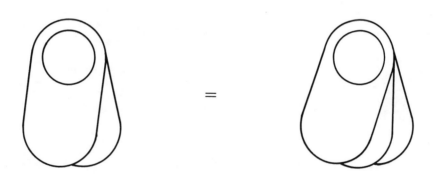

Name the ways 2 weights on one number can balance 3 weights on another number.

1.

2.

3.

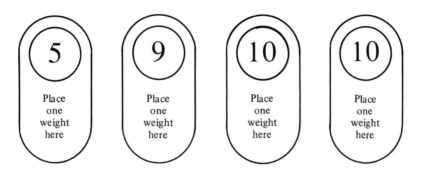

Circle the numbers below that can be balanced with the above weights.

1	2	3	4	5	6	7	8	9	10
11	12	13	14	15	16	17	18	19	20
21	22	23	24	25	26	27	28	29	30
31	32	33	34	35	36	37	38	39	40

TASK 60
Multiplication Logic

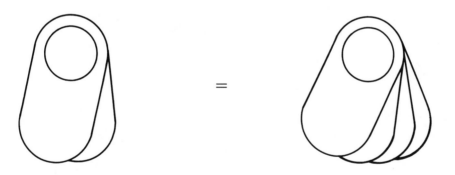

Name the ways 2 weights on one number can balance 4 weights on another number.

1.

2.

3.

4.

5.

Name the ways three weights on same number can balance 4 weights on another number

1.

2.

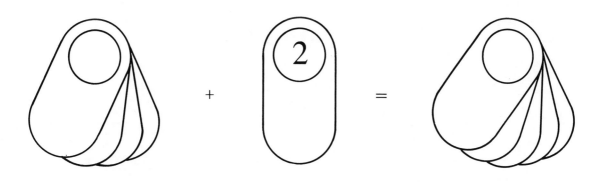

Name the ways four weights on one number plus one weight on 2 can be balanced by five weights on one number.

1.

2.

Name the ways four weights on one number can balance five weights on another number.

1.

2.

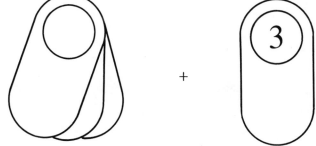 +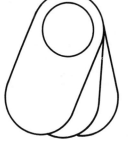

Name the ways three weights on one number plus one weight on 3 can be balanced by three weights on one number.

1.

2.

3.

4.

5.

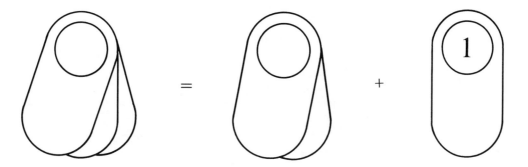

Name the ways three weights on one number can balance two weights on one number plus a weight on 1.

1.

2.

3.

4.

Will these balance?

3

8 weights

Estimate: YES ____   NO ____

Answer: YES ____   NO ____

5

5 weights

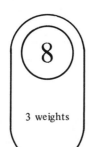

8

3 weights

Estimate: YES ____   NO ____

Answer: YES ____   NO ____

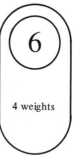

6

4 weights

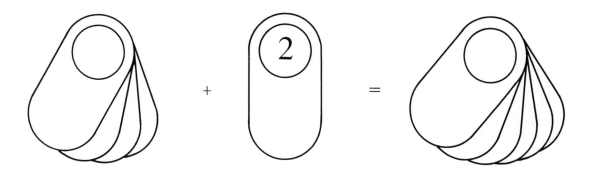

Name the ways four weights on one numeral plus one weight on 2 can be balanced by six weights on one number.

1.

2.

3.

4.

Will these balance?

3

8 weights

4

7 weights

Estimate: YES ____   NO ____
Answer: YES ____   NO ____

8

5 weights

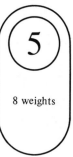

5

8 weights

Estimate: YES ____   NO ____
Answer: YES ____   NO ____

Where do the weights go?

?
2 weights

Estimate _____
Answer _____

5
4 weights

?
10 weights

Estimate _____
Answer _____

5
2 weights

Where do the weights go?

?
3 weights

Estimate _____
Answer _____

2
6 weights

?
4 weights

Estimate _____
Answer _____

6
2 weights

Where do the weights go?

?

8 weights

Estimate _____

Answer _____

8

7 weights

?

4 weights

Estimate _____

Answer _____

3

9 weights

Where do the weights go?

?

6 weights

Estimate _____

Answer _____

6

3 weights

?

6 weights

Estimate _____

Answer _____

2

9 weights

How many weights are needed?

9

? weights

Estimate _____
Answer _____

6

6 weights

4

? weights

Estimate _____
Answer _____

6

6 weights

- -

How many weights are needed?

4

? weights

Estimate _____
Answer _____

8

2 weights

3

? weights

Estimate _____
Answer _____

5

3 weights

How many weights are needed?

4
? weights

Estimate _____
Answer _____

8
6 weights

10
? weights

Estimate _____
Answer _____

5
6 weights

How many weights are needed?

2
? weights

Estimate _____
Answer _____

6
3 weights

5
? weights

Estimate _____
Answer _____

10
4 weights

Balance 8

Place weights on 2 and 3 only.

Answer: _____ = 8

Place weights on 2 or 3.

Answer: _____ = 8

Place no weights on 2 or 3.

Answer: _____ = 8

Balance 16

Place weights on 3 and 4 only.

Answer: _____ = 16

Place weights on 3 or 4.

Answer: _____ = 16

Place no weights on 3 or 4.

Answer: _____ = 16

Balance 12

Place weights on 2 and 3 only.

Answer: _____ = 12

Place weights on 2 or 3.

Answer: _____ = 12

Place no weights on 2 or 3.

Answer: _____ = 12

Balance 20

Place weights on 3 and 5 only.

Answer: _____ = 20

Place weights on 3 or 5.

Answer: _____ = 20

Place no weights on 3 or 5.

Answer: _____ = 20

Balance 24

Place weights on 9 and 6 only.

Answer: _____ = 24

Place weights on 9 or 6.

Answer: _____ = 24

Place no weights on 9 or 6.

Answer: _____ = 24

Balance 21

Place weights on 3, 4, and 5 only.

Answer: _____ = 21

Place weights on 3, 4, or 5.

Answer: _____ = 21

Place no weights on 3, 4, or 5.

Answer: _____ = 21

Balance 25

Place weights on 2 and 5 only.

Answer: _____ = 25

Place weights on 2 or 5.

Answer: _____ = 25

Place no weights on 2 or 5.

Answer: _____ = 25

TASK 84
And/or Logic

Balance 27

Place weights on 3, 4, and 5 only.

Answer: _____ = 27

Place weights on 3, 4, or 5.

Answer: _____ = 27

Place no weights on 3, 4, or 5.

Answer: _____ = 27

Balance 28

Place weights on 4, 5, and 6 only.

Answer: _____ = 28

Place weights on 4 or 5 or 6.

Answer: _____ = 28

Place no weights on 4 or 5 or 6.

Answer: _____ = 28

Can you balance 12 with weights only on . . .

1	YES ☐	NO ☐		6	YES ☐	NO ☐	
2	YES ☐	NO ☐		7	YES ☐	NO ☐	
3	YES ☐	NO ☐		8	YES ☐	NO ☐	
4	YES ☐	NO ☐		9	YES ☐	NO ☐	
5	YES ☐	NO ☐		10	YES ☐	NO ☐	

Balance 30

Place weights on 4, 5, and 6 only.

Answer: _____ = 30

Place weights on 4 or 5 or 6.

Answer: _____ = 30

Place no weights on 4 or 5 or 6.

Answer: _____ = 30

Can you balance 13 with weights only on . . .

1	YES ☐	NO ☐		6	YES ☐	NO ☐
2	YES ☐	NO ☐		7	YES ☐	NO ☐
3	YES ☐	NO ☐		8	YES ☐	NO ☐
4	YES ☐	NO ☐		9	YES ☐	NO ☐
5	YES ☐	NO ☐		10	YES ☐	NO ☐

Can you balance 14 with weights only on . . .

1	YES ☐	NO ☐☐☐	6	YES ☐	NO ☐
2	YES ☐	NO ☐	7	YES ☐	NO ☐
3	YES ☐	NO ☐	8	YES ☐	NO ☐
4	YES ☐	NO ☐	9	YES ☐	NO ☐
5	YES ☐	NO ☐	10	YES ☐	NO ☐

Can you balance 16 with weights only on . . .

1	YES ☐	NO ☐	6	YES ☐	NO ☐
2	YES ☐	NO ☐	7	YES ☐	NO ☐
3	YES ☐	NO ☐	8	YES ☐	NO ☐
4	YES ☐	NO ☐	9	YES ☐	NO ☐
5	YES ☐	NO ☐	10	YES ☐	NO ☐

Can you balance 15 with weights only on . . .

1	YES	☐	NO	☐	6	YES	☐	NO	☐
2	YES	☐	NO	☐	7	YES	☐	NO	☐
3	YES	☐	NO	☐	8	YES	☐	NO	☐
4	YES	☐	NO	☐	9	YES	☐	NO	☐
5	YES	☐	NO	☐	10	YES	☐	NO	☐☐

Can you balance 18 with weights only on . . .

1	YES	☐	NO	☐	6	YES	☐	NO	☐
2	YES	☐	NO	☐	7	YES	☐	NO	☐
3	YES	☐	NO	☐	8	YES	☐	NO	☐
4	YES	☐	NO	☐☐	9	YES	☐	NO	☐
5	YES	☐	NO	☐	10	YES	☐	NO	☐

Color "yes" answers from activities 86 to 92.

	1	2	3	4	5	6	7	8	9	10
12										
13										
14										
15										
16										
18										

- -

What factors are the same?

12 and 13 _____   16 and 12 _____
12 and 14 _____   16 and 13 _____
12 and 15 _____   16 and 14 _____
12 and 16 _____   16 and 15 _____
12 and 18 _____   16 and 18 _____

15 and 12 _____   14 and 12 _____
15 and 13 _____   14 and 13 _____
15 and 14 _____   14 and 15 _____
15 and 16 _____   14 and 16 _____
15 and 18 _____   14 and 18 _____

These drawings of math balance weights can be cut out and glued on blank activity cards:

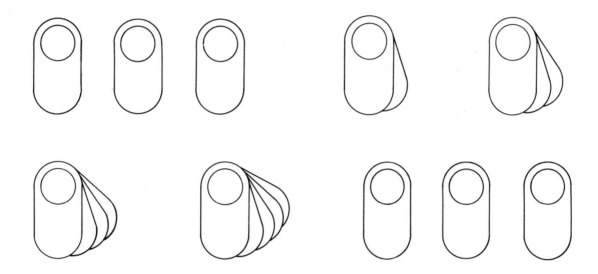

These drawings of math balance weights can be cut out and glued on blank activity cards:

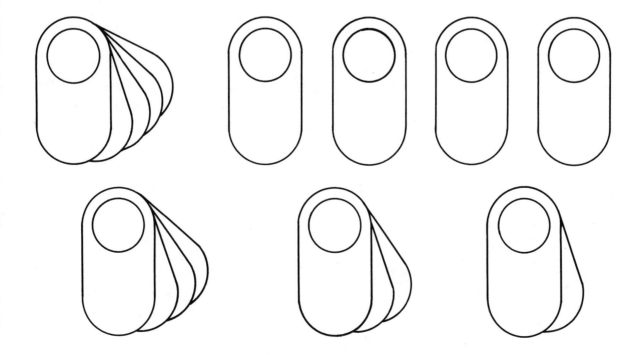

Other Names

19. Balance 12

20. Balance 16

21. Balance 18

22. Balance 9

Tens

23. Other Names for 10
24. Other Names for 10
25. Other Names for 10
26. Other Names for 10
27. Other Names for 10
28. Other Names for 10
29. Missing addends for 10
30. Missing addends for 10

Division

31. Two as divisor, no remainders
32. Three as divisor, no remainders
33. Four as divisor, no remainders
34. Five as divisor, no remainders
35. Six as divisor, no remainders
36. Seven as divisor, no remainders
37. Eight as divisor, no remainders
38. Nine as divisor, no remainders
39. Twelve as dividend, no remainders
40. Twenty-four as dividend, no remainders
41. Five as divisor, remainders
42. Five as divisor, remainders

Place Value

43. Two as place value unit
44. Five as place value unit
45. Three as place value unit
46. Eight as place value unit

Coloring Patterns

47. Patterns with two's

48. Patterns with three's

49. Patterns with four's

50. Patterns with five's

Addition Problem Solving

51. Addition problem solving to ten

52. Addition problem solving to ten

53. Addition problem solving to ten

54. Addition problem solving to ten

55. Addition problem solving to twenty

56. Addition problem solving to twenty

57. Addition problem solving to thirty

58. Addition problem solving to forty

Logic in Balancing

Balance?

And/Or Logic

Factors

Student Designed Activity Cards

Completed Activities

Blank Activity Cards

Drawings of Math Balance Weights

Directions and Answers

iend's Name _____ Name _____

Date _____

Title of Activity _____

Friend's Name _____ Name _____

Date _____

Title of Activity _____